Other Books by Bill Watterson

Calvin and Hobbes
Something Under the Bed Is Drooling
Yukon Ho!
Weirdos From Another Planet!
The Revenge of the Baby-Sat
Scientific Progress Goes "Boink"

Treasury Collections

The Essential Calvin and Hobbes
The Calvin and Hobbes Lazy Sunday Book
The Authoritative Calvin and Hobbes

ATTACK OF THE Deranged Mutant Killer Monster SNOW GOONS

A Calvin and Hobbes Collection by Bill Watterson

SCHOLASTIC INC.
New York Toronto London Auckland Sydney

Calvin and Hobbes is distributed internationally
by Universal Press Syndicate.

ISBN 0-590-46229-6

60 59 58 57 56 55 54 53 52 51 50 49   14 15 /0

Printed in the U.S.A.   34

First Scholastic printing, September 1992

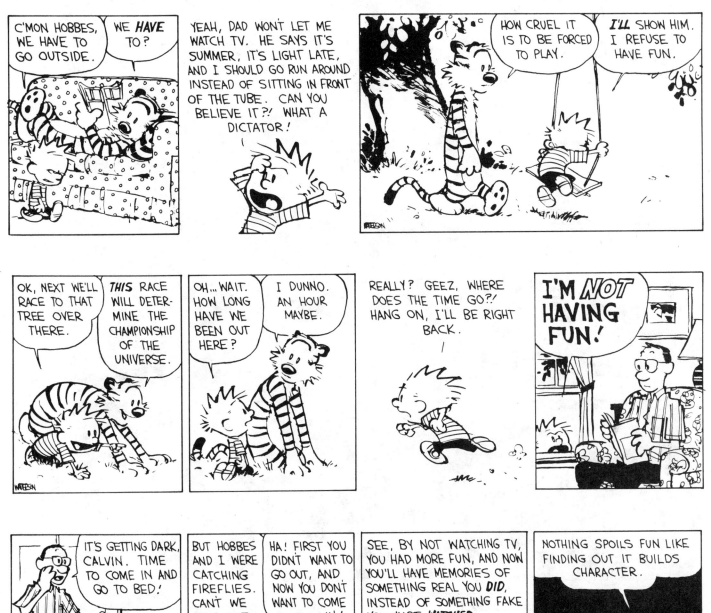

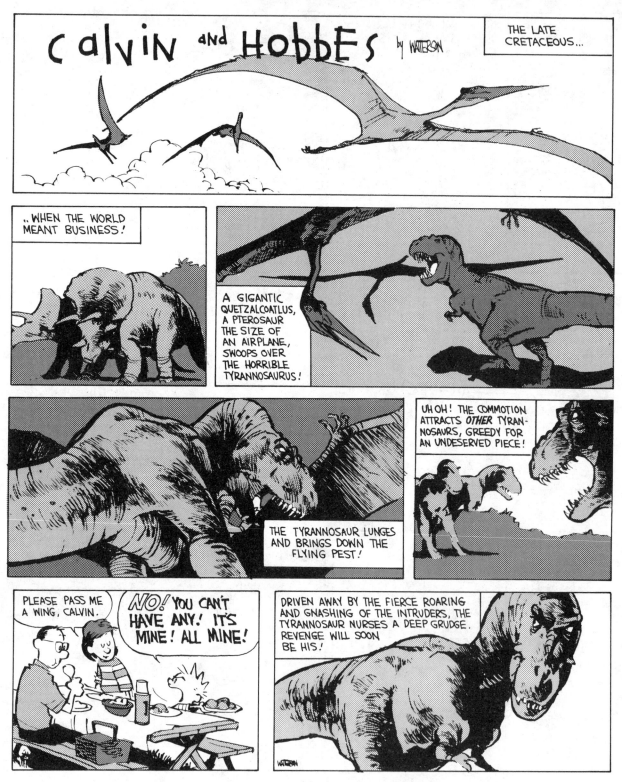

14

My tiger, it seems, is running 'round nude.
This fur coat must have made him perspire.
It lies on the floor—should this be construed
As a permanent change of attire?
Perhaps he considers its colors passé,
Or maybe it fit him too snug
Will he want it back? Should I put it away?
Or use it right here as a rug?

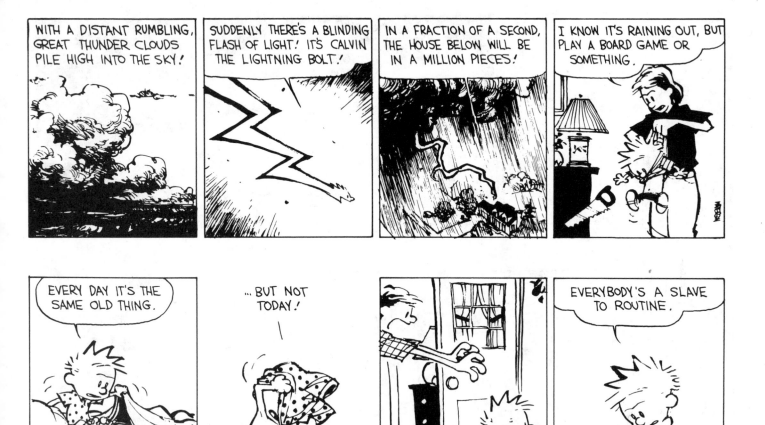

28

THERE! I FINISHED OUR SECRET CODE!

LET'S SEE.

I ASSIGNED EACH LETTER A TOTALLY RANDOM NUMBER, SO THE CODE WILL BE HARD TO CRACK. FOR LETTER "A," YOU WRITE 3,004,572,688. "B" IS 28,731,569½.

THAT'S A GOOD CODE ALL RIGHT.

NOW WE JUST COMMIT THIS TO MEMORY.

DID YOU FINISH YOUR MAP OF OUR NEIGHBORHOOD?

NOT YET. HOW MANY BRICKS DOES THE FRONT WALK HAVE?

WE'VE GOT OUR MAP, OUR CODE, AND OUR WATER BALLOON! LET'S GO SOAK SUSIE!

OUR MAP SAYS FIRST WE RUN TO THE BIG TREE OUT BACK.

NOW TO THE BUSH OUT FRONT!

NOW TO THE DITCH OUT BACK!

NOW TO THE TREE OUT FRONT!

IN CASE YOU'RE WONDERING ...THIS IS TO LOSE ANYONE WHO MIGHT BE TAILING US.

I'M WRITING YOU A MESSAGE IN CODE. HOW DO YOU SPELL "NINCOMPOOP"?

WE MADE IT TO SUSIE'S YARD!

BUT WHERE'S SUSIE? I DON'T SEE HER!

ARGHH! WE GO TO ALL THIS TROUBLE TO LAUNCH AN ATTACK ON HER, AND WHAT DOES SHE DO? SHE MOVES! ALL OUR GREAT PLANS ARE FOR NAUGHT! A WHOLE MORNING RUINED!

MAYBE SHE JUST WENT IN FOR LUNCH. SEE, SHE LEFT SOME OF HER TOYS OUT, SO SHE'S PROBABLY PLANNING TO COME BACK.

THAT GIVES ME A FABULOUS IDEA!

UH OH.

40

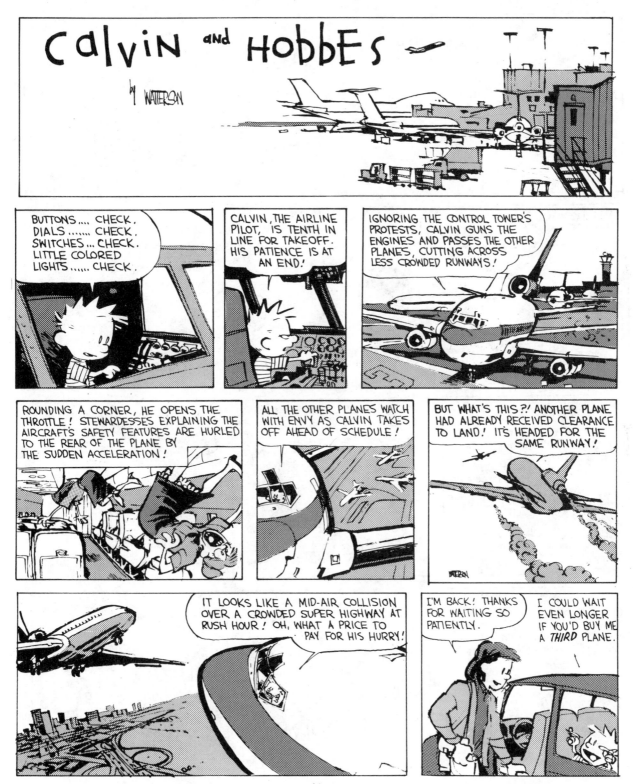

47

EVERYONE TAKES ME FOR GRANTED! NOBODY PAYS ANY ATTENTION TO MY NEEDS!

IS IT TOO MUCH TO ASK FOR AN OCCASIONAL TOKEN GESTURE OF APPRECIATION?!

OK, HOW ABOUT A BIG HUG?

COULD I HAVE 20 DOLLARS?

SEE?! I DON'T MATTER TO ANYONE! NOBODY CARES ABOUT ME!

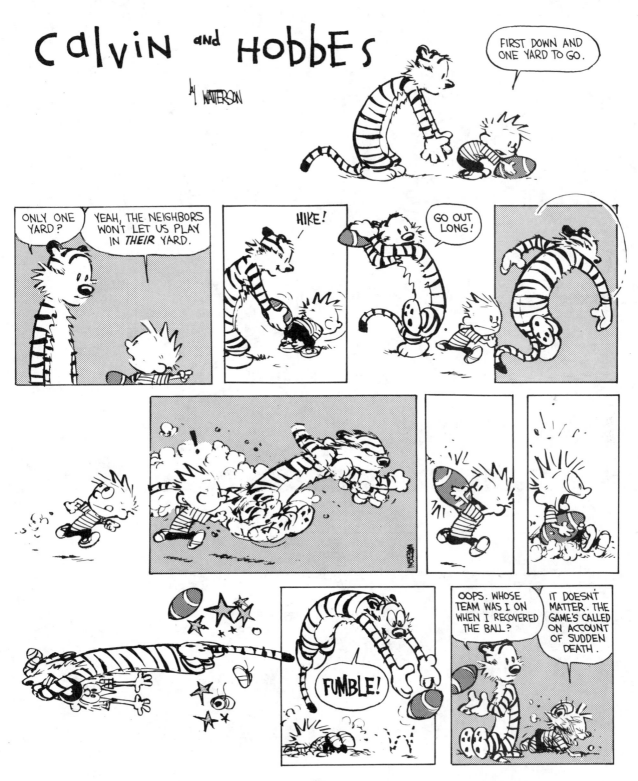

ON THE ONE HAND, IT'S A GOOD SIGN FOR US ARTISTS THAT, IN THIS AGE OF VISUAL BOMBARDMENT FROM ALL MEDIA, A SIMPLE DRAWING CAN PROVOKE AND SHOCK VIEWERS. IT CONFIRMS THAT IMAGES STILL HAVE POWER.

ON THE OTHER HAND, MY TEACHER'S REACTIONARY GRADING SHOWS THAT OUR SOCIETY IS CULTURALLY ILLITERATE AND THAT MANY PEOPLE CAN'T TELL GOOD ART FROM A HOLE IN THE GROUND.

THIS DRAWING I DID OBVIOUSLY CHALLENGES THE KNOW-NOTHING COMPLACENCY OF THOSE WHO PREFER SAFE, PREDIGESTED, BUCOLIC GENRE SCENES.

MY "C-" FIRMLY ESTABLISHES ME ON THE CUTTING EDGE OF THE AVANT-GARDE.

DON'T YOU HAVE TO WEAR SILLY CLOTHES THEN?

THE HARD PART FOR US AVANT-GARDE POST-MODERN ARTISTS IS DECIDING WHETHER OR NOT TO EMBRACE COMMERCIALISM.

DO WE ALLOW OUR WORK TO BE HYPED AND EXPLOITED BY A MARKET THAT'S SIMPLY HUNGRY FOR THE NEXT NEW THING? DO WE PARTICIPATE IN A SYSTEM THAT TURNS HIGH ART INTO LOW ART SO IT'S BETTER SUITED FOR MASS CONSUMPTION?

OF COURSE, WHEN AN ARTIST GOES COMMERCIAL, HE MAKES A MOCKERY OF HIS STATUS AS AN OUTSIDER AND FREE THINKER. HE BUYS INTO THE CRASS AND SHALLOW VALUES ART SHOULD TRANSCEND. HE TRADES THE INTEGRITY OF HIS ART FOR RICHES AND FAME.

OH, WHAT THE HECK. I'LL DO IT.

THAT WASN'T SO HARD.

TODAY I DREW ANOTHER PICTURE IN MY "DINOSAURS IN ROCKET SHIPS" SERIES, AND MISS WORMWOOD THREATENED TO GIVE ME A BAD MARK IN HER GRADE BOOK IF I DIDN'T STOP!

THE ARTS ARE UNDER ATTACK! FREEDOM OF EXPRESSION IS BEING SQUELCHED!

THE AUTHORITIES ARE TRYING TO SILENCE ANY VIEW CONTRARY TO THEIR OWN!

WHAT DOES YOUR TEACHER OBJECT TO ABOUT DINOSAURS?

MOSTLY MY DRAWING THEM DURING MATH.

61

68

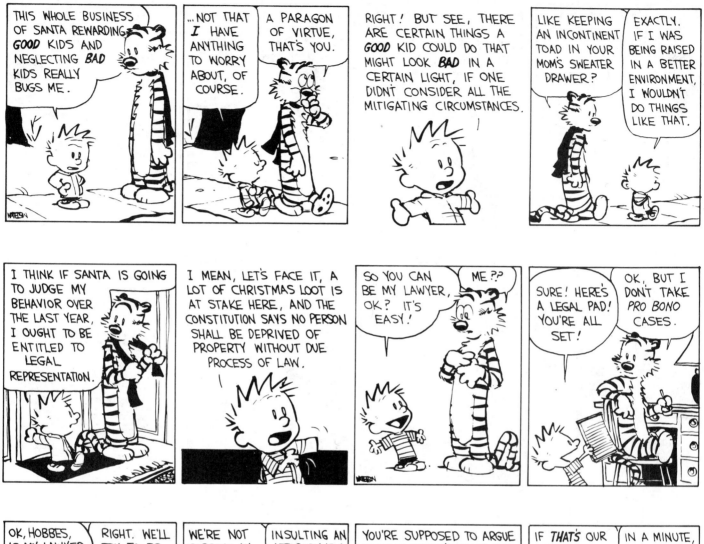

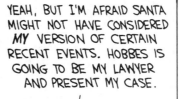

SO LONG, MOM! HOBBES AND I ARE OFF TO THE NORTH POLE! — THE NORTH POLE?

YEP! WE'RE GOING TO SEE SANTA. — HOW COME? YOU ALREADY SENT HIM YOUR CHRISTMAS LIST.

YEAH, BUT I'M AFRAID SANTA MIGHT NOT HAVE CONSIDERED *MY* VERSION OF CERTAIN RECENT EVENTS. HOBBES IS GOING TO BE MY LAWYER AND PRESENT MY CASE.

JUST HOW RECENT ARE THESE RECENT EVENTS YOU'RE TALKING ABOUT? — GOTTA GO, MOM. IT'S A LONG WALK.

OK, HERE'S OUR STRATEGY: WHEN WE GET TO THE NORTH POLE, WE TELL SANTA THAT I'VE BEEN THE VICTIM OF MALICIOUS SLANDERS BY MY ENEMIES, AND WE'RE APPEALING TO HIM FOR JUSTICE.

WE SAY THAT I'M REALLY A *GOOD* KID... A GOOD KID WITH A GOOD HEART!

WE SAY I'M GOOD, GOOD, GOOD FROM THE MOMENT I GET UP UNTIL... — HEY! THERE'S SUSIE!

...UNTIL THE MOMENT A THOUGHT ENTERS YOUR HEAD. — I DON'T THINK SHE SAW US! QUICK, PACK SOME SLUSH-BALLS!

SUSIE'S STILL CONCENTRATING ON HER SNOWMAN! LET'S SNEAK UP AND BARRAGE HER WITH SLUSHBALLS!

TWO MINUTES AGO WE WERE ON OUR WAY TO TELL SANTA HOW *GOOD* YOU ARE, REMEMBER? HAVE YOU LOST YOUR MARBLES?! — OOPS. I FORGOT.

HOW MANY PRESENTS DO YOU THINK I'D FORFEIT FOR JUST ONE CLEAN SMACK UPSIDE SUSIE'S HEAD?

WELL, THE SHOPPING IS DONE, THE PRESENTS ARE WRAPPED AND SENT, AND CALVIN'S IN BED. FOR THE FIRST TIME THIS MONTH, THERE'S NOTHING THAT HAS TO BE DONE.

I KNOW... SOMETIMES THIS SEASON REALLY SEEMS OUT OF CONTROL. WE DON'T OFTEN THINK ABOUT WHAT IT'S ALL SUPPOSED TO MEAN.

MM-HMM. IT'S GOOD TO SIT BY A COZY FIRE AND TAKE SOME QUIET TIME TO REFLECT.

WHAT'S *THIS*?! SANTA FLAMBÉ??

PSST! WAKE UP! MERRY CHRISTMAS, OL' BUDDY!

MERRY CHRISTMAS.

I DIDN'T GET YOU A PRESENT, BUT YOU'RE MY BEST FRIEND IN THE WORLD, HOBBES.

YOU'RE MY BEST FRIEND, TOO. I THINK THAT'S A GREAT GIFT.

WELL, ENOUGH OF THAT! IT'S ALMOST 4 AM! LET'S WAKE MOM AND DAD AND SEE WHAT SANTA BROUGHT US!

REMEMBER WE AGREED THAT IF SANTA GAVE YOU ANY SALMON, YOU'D SHARE IT!

Dear Grandma,
    Thank you for the nice box of crayons you sent me for Christmas.

THIS IS PROMPT.

OH YEAH, I ALWAYS SEND GRANDMA A THANK-YOU NOTE RIGHT AWAY.

...EVER SINCE SHE SENT ME THAT EMPTY BOX WITH THE SARCASTIC NOTE SAYING SHE WAS JUST CHECKING TO SEE IF THE POSTAL SERVICE WAS STILL WORKING.

Panel 1: THIS WILL BE THE STRONGEST SNOW FORT EVER BUILT!

Panel 2: UGHH NGGHH

Panel 3: RGHH MNHG UNNHH

Panel 4: THERE! WE'RE SAFE FROM THAT SNOW GOON *NOW!* / I WONDER WHY WE HAVEN'T SEEN HIM FOR A WHILE.

Panel 5: HI CALVIN. NICE SNOW FORT. / I'LL SAY! THE WALLS ARE TWO FEET THICK AND WE'VE GOT 50 SNOWBALLS IN HERE!

Panel 6: WHO ARE YOU FIGHTING? / THERE'S A SNOW GOON RUNNING LOOSE! IF I WERE YOU, I WOULDN'T STICK AROUND. THIS COULD GET UGLY.

Panel 7: WHAT'S A SNOW GOON? / IT'S LIKE A SNOW MAN, BUT A GROTESQUE, EVIL, DEMENTED MONSTER.

Panel 8: OH, IS *THAT* WHAT ALL THOSE UGLY THINGS YOU MADE IN THE FRONT YARD ARE? / WHAT DO YOU MEAN, "ALL THOSE"?

Panel 9: LOOK! A *NEW* SNOW GOON! / THAT'S NOT THE ONE I MADE!

Panel 10: THE ORIGINAL SNOW GOON MUST BE MAKING HIS *OWN* SNOW GOONS! / OH NO!

Panel 11: I'LL BET HE'S MAKING AN ARMY! IN A FEW DAYS, HE COULD BUILD A HUNDRED SNOW GOONS! IF EACH OF *THEM* BUILT *ANOTHER* HUNDRED, AND THEN *THOSE* ALL BUILT A HUNDRED *MORE*, WHY...

Panel 12: ...THAT WOULD BE PRETTY COOL, IF THEY WEREN'T OUT TO KILL ME. / I VOTE WE MAKE TRACKS FOR FLORIDA.

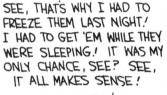

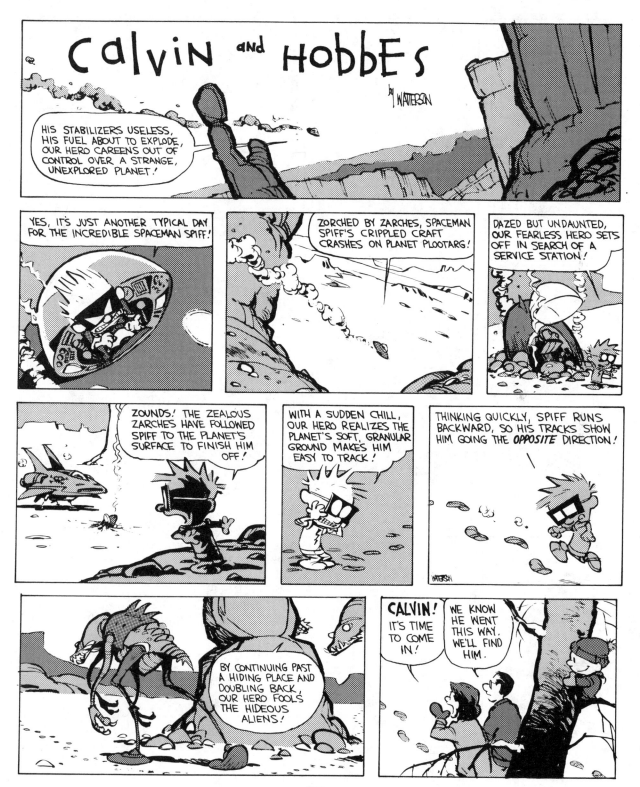

I THINK GROWN-UPS JUST *ACT* LIKE THEY KNOW WHAT THEY'RE DOING.

WHAT HAVE YOU GOT TO SAY FOR YOURSELF?

DON'T TOUCH ANYTHING. I'M LOOKING FOR CLUES.

THE CLICK OF A HAMMER BEING COCKED BEHIND MY HEAD FOCUSED MY THOUGHTS LIKE ONLY A LOADED .38 CAN.

THE DAME HAD SET ME UP! SHE DIDN'T WANT ME TO SOLVE THE CASE AT ALL! SHE JUST WANTED A PATSY TO PIN THE CRIME ON!

WELL?

I DIDN'T LIKE THE WAY THIS STORY WAS SHAPING UP, SO I DECIDED TO WRITE A NEW ENDING WITH MY .45 AUTOMATIC AS CO-AUTHOR.

I INTRODUCED THE DAME TO A FRIEND WHO'S VERY CLOSE TO MY HEART. JUST A LITTLE DOWN AND LEFT, TO BE SPECIFIC.

MY FRIEND IS AN ELOQUENT SPEAKER. HE MADE THREE PROFOUND ARGUMENTS WHILE I EXCUSED MYSELF FROM THE ROOM. I ALWAYS LEAVE WHEN THE TALK GETS PHILOSOPHICAL.

YOU'RE IN *REAL* TROUBLE NOW, YOUNG MAN!!

I'D JUST FINISHED PUTTING THE PUZZLE PIECES TOGETHER WHEN THE DAME'S HIRED GOON JUMPED OUT OF NOWHERE AND PRACTICED FOR HIS CHIROPRACTIC DEGREE.

WHEN HE WAS DONE, AN ALL-PERCUSSION SYMPHONY WAS PLAYING IN MY HEAD, AND THE ACOUSTICS WERE INCREDIBLE. THE ORCHESTRA WENT ON A TEN-CITY TOUR OF MY BRAIN, AND I HAD A SEASON PASS WITH FRONT ROW SEATS.

I HAD FIGURED OUT WHO TRASHED THE DAME'S LIVING ROOM, BUT SINCE SHE WASN'T MY CLIENT ANY MORE, I FELT NO NEED TO DIVULGE THE INFORMATION.

BESIDES, THE CULPRIT HAPPENED TO BE A BUDDY OF MINE. I CLOSED THE CASE.

I GUESS WE SHOULD'VE PLAYED OUTSIDE, HUH?

Row 1:

WHAT'S UP TODAY?

NOTHING SO FAR.

"SO FAR"?

WELL, YOU NEVER KNOW. SOMETHING *COULD* HAPPEN TODAY.

AND IF ANYTHING *DOES*, BY GOLLY, I'M GOING TO BE READY FOR IT!

I NEED A SUIT LIKE THAT.

Row 2:

I JUST SAW A COMMERCIAL FOR A LUXURY CRUISE. HOW COME *WE* DON'T EVER GO ON VACATIONS LIKE THAT?

VACATIONS ARE ALL JUST A MATTER OF COMPARISON.

HUH?

WE SPEND A WEEK IN COLD, UNCOMFORTABLE TENTS EACH YEAR SO LIVING *HERE* THE REST OF THE TIME SEEMS LIKE A LUXURY CRUISE. IF YOUR TRIPS ARE UNPLEASANT, YOUR WHOLE *LIFE* IS A VACATION!

PLEASE TELL ME I'M ADOPTED.

Row 3:

YOU KNOW, I DON'T THINK MATH IS A SCIENCE. I THINK IT'S A RELIGION.

A RELIGION?

YEAH. ALL THESE EQUATIONS ARE LIKE MIRACLES. YOU TAKE TWO NUMBERS AND WHEN YOU ADD THEM, THEY MAGICALLY BECOME ONE *NEW* NUMBER! NO ONE CAN SAY HOW IT HAPPENS. YOU EITHER BELIEVE IT OR YOU DON'T.

THIS WHOLE BOOK IS FULL OF THINGS THAT HAVE TO BE ACCEPTED ON FAITH! IT'S A RELIGION!

AND IN THE PUBLIC SCHOOLS NO LESS. CALL A LAWYER.

AS A MATH ATHEIST, I SHOULD BE EXCUSED FROM THIS.

The End